Civics Today

Citizenship, Economics, & You

Interpreting Political Cartoons

Glencoe
McGraw-Hill

New York, New York   Columbus, Ohio   Chicago, Illinois   Peoria, Illinois   Woodland Hills, California

Glencoe/McGraw-Hill

A Division of The **McGraw·Hill** Companies

Send all inquiries to:
Glencoe/McGraw-Hill
8787 Orion Place
Columbus, OH 43240-4027

ISBN 0-07-830780-5

Printed in the United States of America

4 5 6 7 8 9 10   047   07 06 05

Table of Contents

Introduction v

1. The Clash of Ideas and Actions 1
2. Columbus, Then and Now 3
3. Franklin's Albany Plan of Union and The First Political Cartoon 5
4. A Soldier's Life Never Changes 7
5. The Embargo Act of 1807 9
6. The Gerrymander, Past and Present 11
7. Andrew Jackson and the Second Bank of the United States 13
8. War on the Horizon 15
9. Reconstruction and Carpetbaggers 17
10. Thomas Nast: America's Greatest Political Cartoonist 19
11. Nast on Native Americans 21
12. Urban Corruption 23
13. Industrialization and Urban Politics 25
14. A Nation of Immigrants: A Cartoonist on Changing Times 27
15. Battle Against the Trusts 29
16. A Populist View of President McKinley 31
17. Yellow Journalism 33
18. Big Stick Diplomacy in the Western Hemisphere 35
19. Women Campaign for Suffrage 37
20. A League Not of Our Own 39
21. The Gates to Immigration Close 41
22. Native Americans and a Nation of Immigrants 43
23. The Great Depression 45
24. The New Deal 47
25. World War II 49
26. Joseph McCarthy and the Red Scare 51
27. The Death of JFK 53
28. Vietnam 55
29. Nixon on Civil Rights 57
30. Achieving Equality for Women 59
31. Questioning Cultural Values 61
32. Piercing the Reagan Doctrine 63
33. Environmental Awareness 65
34. Third Parties 67
35. The Decline of Communism 69
36. Apathy Among American Voters 71

Answer Key 73

Introduction

POLITICAL CARTOONS: SERIOUS FUN

I don't mind what people write about me.
Most of my constituents can't read.
But oh, those damn pictures!
—Boss Tweed

In general, political cartoons engage us in the serious fun called satire. **Satire** uses humor to lower something or someone in the reader's or viewer's estimation. At its best, satire is not mean-spirited, and its point is not to harm. Rather, satire exposes human folly to make room for improvement.

Political cartoons have characteristic **contents, methods,** and **purposes.** The **content** of political cartoons is anything political, but the best cartoons deal with universal themes, either because an event itself is so profound—women gaining the right to vote, for example—or because the cartoon deals with a deeper meaning of the issue of the day—a civil rights march is connected to slavery and the Declaration of Independence, for example.

Political cartoons use a number of **methods** in the service of satire: **caricature, symbolism, metaphor, irony, sarcasm,** and **stereotyping. Caricature** works by suggestion and exaggeration, usually by exaggerating one feature of a person or thing. These highlighted features identify the person or thing, but they also say something about the person's or thing's character, beliefs, actions, or significance. Exaggerating Ronald Reagan's thick black hair, for example, makes a point about his well-cultivated image of youthful energy.

A **symbol** represents something else: a dove represents peace, for example. Often a symbol is a material object (e.g., Statue of Liberty) that represents something abstract or invisible (freedom). A **metaphor** uses an object to note a similarity to something else. Using a tiger to represent one nation invading another nation is metaphorical: tigers and nations are different, but a country acts like a tiger when it pounces on and swallows up another country.

Irony expresses an idea through a contradiction between something's literal meaning and the intended meaning. Putting a crown on a U.S. president is ironic. The ironic clash between the literal meaning of the crown—a sign of royalty—and the intended meaning—a president has overstepped the boundaries of legitimate democratic power—is expressed by the contradiction of putting a crown on the president's head. This clash adds force to the message. **Sarcasm** is a form of irony. The element that turns irony into sarcasm is the appearance of mockery, or bitterness. Drawing the kingly president as a gluttonous Henry the VIII, with a cabinet of fawning courtiers and a dungeon full of peasants, turns the cartoon into sarcasm. **Stereotypes** work by taking a real or imagined trait of an individual to be true of the group to which the individual belongs. Typically, stereotypes are dangerous because they express bias by imagining traits or generalizing unfairly in order to exercise power in a way that harms others.

Political cartoonists are idealistic crusaders who "reprimand" the world and people for falling short. The **purpose** of most political cartoons is to expose one of two gaps: that between appearance and reality, and that between what is and what should or could be. Thus, political cartoons often expose hypocrisy, point out pretentiousness, laugh at arrogance, deflate the powerful, and give voice to the underdog. That they do such serious things through humor and fun is part of their appeal. The lighthearted genre of the cartoon adds a little sugar to the serious political medicine that is the cartoon's message. In this way, political cartoons also say that we might be better off taking ourselves less seriously, all the while insisting that we live up to our better selves—as people and as citizens.

INTERPRETING POLITICAL CARTOONS

Activity 1

THE CLASH OF IDEAS AND ACTIONS

History tends to record the deeds of the rich and powerful. It often does not pay such attention to the lives and feelings of the common people. Battles supposedly fought for the welfare of the people often are only remotely concerned with those people. As we will see in this book, the difference between what people said they were fighting for and what they actually wanted has given cartoonists throughout our history much of their best material. This clash of our nation's ideals with its actions is the basis for many of our political cartoons.

DIRECTIONS: The cartoon below gives one view of the clash of ideas and actions. Study the cartoon, and then answer the questions that follow.

"THEY SAY IT'S A BATTLE FOR *OUR* MINDS!"

Reprinted with the permission of Simon & Schuster, Inc., from *Ed Fisher's First Folio* by Edwin Z. Fisher. © 1959 by Ed Fisher.

(continued)

ANALYZING THE CARTOON

1. What is the cartoonist's view of the battle that is about to be fought? Which side does the cartoonist favor? How do you know this?

_____

_____

2. What is the attitude of the people on the hill?

_____

_____

3. How does the cartoonist use the posture and the words of the people on the hill to show that attitude?

_____

_____

_____

CRITICAL THINKING

4. **Analyzing Information** When cartoonists use humor to explore human weakness, they use a device called "satire." Satire exaggerates to poke fun at people. How is the cartoonist using satire in this cartoon? At whom is he poking fun? What weaknesses does he explore?

_____

_____

_____

5. **Applying Information** For which episodes in our modern history might such a cartoon be relevant?

_____

_____

6. **Drawing Conclusions** Provide an example of how a cartoon today uses satire to comment on current political events. Bring to class an example of a recent cartoon in which satire is used to poke fun at a political leader or to make a statement about an important political issue. In the space below, explain how the cartoon uses satire.

_____

_____

_____

INTERPRETING POLITICAL CARTOONS

INTERPRETING POLITICAL CARTOONS

Activity 2

COLUMBUS, THEN AND NOW

Columbus's landing in the Americas is one of the great turning points in world history. After 1492 the European conquest of much of the Americas began, and the history of the Western Hemisphere became intertwined with the history of the Eastern Hemisphere.

For much of our history, Americans have revered Columbus's accomplishments. However, recent interpretations of Columbus and the effects of his voyages have been more critical. In 1992, when the United States celebrated the 500th anniversary of Columbus's first voyage, the nation had a debate about the value and impact of his voyages.

DIRECTIONS: The two illustrations below give us some insight into our changing views of Columbus and his times. Study the art and cartoon, and then answer the questions that follow.

Frank & Marie-Therese Wood Print Collections, Alexandria, VA.

Reprinted with the permission of Simon & Schuster, Inc., from *Ed Fisher's First Folio* by Edwin Z. Fisher. © 1959 by Ed Fisher.

(continued)

ANALYZING THE CARTOON

1. The engraving at the top shows how one artist in the 1800s pictured Columbus's first landing in the Americas. What details show that the artist saw this as an important event?

   _____

   _____

   _____

2. What is similar about the cartoon and the engraving?

   _____

   _____

   _____

3. In the cartoon, who has landed? Why does the cartoonist use them to make his point?

   _____

   _____

   _____

4. At the right of the engraving, we see Native Americans in awe of the Spaniards. What is happening in the same place in the cartoon? What point is the cartoonist making?

   _____

   _____

   _____

CRITICAL THINKING

5. **Identifying Point of View** What is the view of the cartoonist toward Columbus? Is Columbus the target of the satire? Explain your answer.

   _____

   _____

   _____

   _____

6. **Making Comparisons** Use your school or community library to locate two political cartoons that take opposing views of the same political issue. Bring these cartoons to school and describe what devices the cartoonists use to get their points of view across to the reader.

INTERPRETING POLITICAL CARTOONS

Activity 3

FRANKLIN'S ALBANY PLAN OF UNION AND THE FIRST POLITICAL CARTOON

Benjamin Franklin drew the cartoon below, and it is believed to be the first cartoon published in the United States. He published it in his *Pennsylvania Gazette* on May 9, 1754, just before delegates of the colonists met at the Albany Congress. Franklin hoped it would generate support for his Plan of Union. Franklin's cartoon was later used on flags and posters to support collaborations against British taxation of the colonies under the Stamp Act (1765) and to support revolution (1776).

DIRECTIONS: Study the cartoon below, and then answer the questions that follow.

Library of Congress

(continued)

ANALYZING THE CARTOON

1. Notice the letters next to each piece of the snake. What do these letters stand for?

_____

2. Why does the snake have 8 pieces, and not 13?

_____

3. Which of the following slogans best reflects the general theme of Franklin's cartoon? Circle your response.

   a. In unity there is strength.

   b. The whole is greater than the sum of its parts.

   c. Too many cooks spoil the broth.

4. What message was Franklin's cartoon delivering to the delegates at the Albany Congress?

_____

_____

CRITICAL THINKING

5. **Drawing Conclusions** Is Franklin's message still relevant for political life today? Support your answer with specific references.

_____

_____

6. **Expressing Problems Clearly** When Franklin drew this cartoon, many people mistakenly believed that if a snake were cut into pieces, the pieces could weave themselves back together. Knowing that this is incorrect, write a new caption for the cartoon to replace "Join, or Die." Explain the meaning of your new caption.

_____

_____

7. **Synthesizing Information** If Franklin were alive today, what symbols would he use to send the same message of unity to Americans? Make a list of possible symbols. Compare your list with those of other students in your class. Which symbols appear most frequently? Take a class vote on which symbols best represent the message of American unity.

_____

_____

_____

INTERPRETING POLITICAL CARTOONS

Activity 4

A SOLDIER'S LIFE NEVER CHANGES

Bill Mauldin is one of America's foremost political cartoonists. He first rose to national prominence for his Willie and Joe cartoons in *Stars and Stripes* during World War II, in a feature called "Up Front." Willie and Joe were two average infantrymen. Through them, Mauldin showed and commented on the realities of the war for the common soldier. Mauldin was beloved for how he gave voice to and honored the common soldier in his cartoons.

DIRECTIONS: Study the cartoons below, and then answer the questions that follow.

"Well, no one can accuse us of being mercenaries."

"Interesting lining on your flag here, mister."

(continued)

ANALYZING THE CARTOONS

1. What is a mercenary? Who served as mercenaries in the American Revolution and for which side?

   _____

   _____

2. To what class does the man looking out the window belong? How do you know?

   _____

   _____

3. What about the dress of the soldiers in the left cartoon tells you their low rank?

   _____

   _____

CRITICAL THINKING

4. **Analyzing Information** How well are the soldiers in the left cartoon being paid? How do you know?

   _____

   _____

   _____

5. **Synthesizing Information** In *The American Crisis*, Thomas Paine wrote that, "These are the times that try men's souls. The summer soldier and the sunshine patriot will, in this crisis, shrink from the service of his country. . . ." Explain what Paine means by a "sunshine patriot." Who in these cartoons is a sunshine patriot, and how do you know that?

   _____

   _____

   _____

6. **Making Inferences** Mauldin was commissioned to draw these cartoons to celebrate the anniversary of a famous event of the American Revolution. What was that event? Give evidence for your answer.

   _____

   _____

   _____

INTERPRETING POLITICAL CARTOONS

Activity 5

THE EMBARGO ACT OF 1807

By 1807 the United States found itself in the middle of a dispute between the French and the British. United States ships bound for Europe were often stopped by the British, French, or both. Jefferson hoped to keep the United States neutral. He convinced Congress to pass the Embargo Act of 1807, which made it illegal for United States merchants to import or export goods. Although the embargo hurt both Britain and France, it did more damage at home. New England felt the greatest blow because its economy depended on trade with foreign countries. In this tense environment, the Embargo Act became the subject of many cartoons, pro and con.

DIRECTIONS: The cartoon on this page takes a strong stand on the Embargo Act. Study the cartoon, and then answer the questions that follow.

OGRABME, or, The American Snapping-turtle

Collection of the New York Historical Society, New York.

(continued)

INTERPRETING POLITICAL CARTOONS

ANALYZING THE CARTOON

1. What in this cartoon represents the Embargo Act?

   _____

   _____

2. What does the man with the barrel represent? What is he trying to do?

   _____

   _____

3. To which country does the ship belong? How do you know this? What is the ship waiting for?

   _____

   _____

CRITICAL THINKING

4. **Analyzing Information** Americans had fun playing with the letters of the word *embargo*. What is the meaning of the statement of the smuggler, "Oh! This cursed Ograbme!"?

   _____

   _____

5. **Making Generalizations** Is the cartoonist in favor of or against the Embargo Act? Explain your answer.

   _____

   _____

6. **Drawing Conclusions** Like the smuggler in the cartoon, play with the words "Embargo Act." Create any words or statements that use the letters in "Embargo Act" and might be the caption to a cartoon about the act. You can use any letters more than once. You do not need to use all the letters.

   _____

   _____

7. **Evaluating Information** According to this cartoon, the Embargo Act worked. How well did it work? Support your answer with facts and reasons.

   _____

   _____

   _____

INTERPRETING POLITICAL CARTOONS

Activity 6

THE GERRYMANDER, PAST AND PRESENT

The United States Constitution makes no mention of congressional districts. For most of our history, state legislatures have been responsible for drawing up districts. Sometimes those in power redraw a district to include more voters that agree with them, or to exclude voters who do not agree with them. The practice of selective redrawing is called "gerrymandering," after the creature in the left cartoon. Elkanah Tilsdale drew his "Gerrymander" for the *Boston Gazette* in 1812. A large number of Republicans in one township (Marblehead, the right foot) was able to reelect Governor Gerry despite the Federalist majority against Gerry in all the other townships. This kind of redistricting struck most people as unfair. There was a backlash against the Republicans, and this mutant district was dismantled in 1813. The right cartoon offers a modern take on the same practice.

Directions: Study the cartoons below, and then answer the questions that follow.

Library of Congress

Steve Magnuson Cartoon Art

(continued)

ANALYZING THE CARTOONS

1. What are the cartoonists' attitudes about gerrymandering? Provide evidence for your answer from the drawings.

_____

_____

2. To what does the right cartoon compare a congressional district?

_____

_____

3. Why are the districts in the right cartoon contrasted sharply through the use of black and white shapes?

_____

_____

4. What is the meaning of the right cartoon's title, "Contemporary American Realism #3"?

_____

_____

CRITICAL THINKING

5. **Synthesizing Information** Should states be allowed to shape districts to establish a majority of one ethnic or racial group in them? Why or why not?

_____

_____

6. **Making Comparisons** Which cartoon makes its case more effectively? Why?

_____

_____

7. **Analyzing Information** Explain the origin of the term "gerrymander."

_____

_____

8. **Synthesizing Information** The Fifteenth Amendment to the Constitution says that Americans' right to vote shall not be interfered with "on account of race, color, or previous condition of servitude." What does this mean? How could congressional districting affect this right?

_____

_____

Copyright © by The McGraw-Hill Companies, Inc.

INTERPRETING POLITICAL CARTOONS

INTERPRETING POLITICAL CARTOONS

Activity 7

ANDREW JACKSON AND THE SECOND BANK OF THE UNITED STATES

Andrew Jackson's veto of the charter of the Second Bank of the United States set off a firestorm of protest. Many newspapers, especially in the East, vigorously opposed Jackson's action. It is no coincidence that those newspapers happened to be owned by some of the wealthiest people in the United States who benefited most from the Bank.

Thus, while there are few cartoons from this period supporting Andrew Jackson's battle against the Second Bank of the United States, there are many criticizing him. On this page are two cartoons commenting on Jackson and the Bank.

Directions: Study the cartoons, and then answer the questions that follow.

Library of Congress

Collection of the New York Historical Society, New York.

(continued)

ANALYZING THE CARTOONS

1. The two cartoons on the previous page focus on the same person, Andrew Jackson. How does each cartoon portray Jackson in order to express its support or criticism of his actions against the Second Bank of the United States?

   Bottom cartoon:

   _____

   _____

   Top cartoon:

   _____

   _____

2. How does the bottom cartoon use size to make its statement? What other symbols does it use?

   _____

   _____

3. What symbols does the top cartoon use?

   _____

   _____

CRITICAL THINKING

4. **Drawing Conclusions** Why would the top cartoon stir more emotion in Jackson's day than it does today?

   _____

   _____

   _____

5. **Making Inferences** Which cartoon do you think was more popular in the West? In the East? Which was more popular among farmers? Which was more popular among lawyers?

   _____

   _____

   _____

6. **Expressing Problems Clearly** Working in small groups, find some modern examples of cartoons that show pro and con attitudes of the same person. Present these cartoons to the class, and have the class decide which pair of cartoons is most effective.

INTERPRETING POLITICAL CARTOONS

Activity 8

WAR ON THE HORIZON

The cartoon below was drawn just before the outbreak of the Civil War. The dominant figure is Columbia, a common symbol for the United States from the colonial period until being eclipsed by Uncle Sam in the 1900s. Columbia originated as Liberty, a feminine symbol of freedom drawn by Paul Revere for the masthead of the *Boston Gazette*. Here, Columbia awakes to an unruly classroom. Unfortunately, she could not get control of her "students," and the Civil War was soon raging.

Directions: Study the cartoon below, and then answer the questions that follow.

MISTRESS COLUMBIA, WHO HAS BEEN TAKING A NAP, SUDDENLY WAKES UP AND CALLS HER NOISY SCHOLARS TO ORDER.

Culver Pictures, Inc.

(continued)

ANALYZING THE CARTOON

1. What are the two ways the cartoonist shows who the two groups of students are?

   _____

   _____

2. What point is the cartoonist making by having Columbia just awaken from a nap?

   _____

   _____

3. What lesson has the teacher assigned? How do you know? Why has she assigned this lesson?

   _____

   _____

4. What is the person in the upper right writing on the board? What does it express about the South's position?

   _____

   _____

5. Why is there a map of the United States behind Miss Columbia?

   _____

   _____

CRITICAL THINKING

6. **Making Inferences** What were the scrambling students doing before the teacher woke up? How do you know? What historical event might the cartoonist be referring to with these students?

   _____

   _____

7. **Identifying the Main Idea** Write a title for this cartoon that expresses its main point.

   _____

   _____

8. **Drawing Conclusions** Is this cartoon more sympathetic to the North, South, or neither? Explain.

   _____

   _____

INTERPRETING POLITICAL CARTOONS

Activity 9

RECONSTRUCTION AND CARPETBAGGERS

As the South began to rebuild after the Civil War, opposition arose among white Southerners to the Reconstruction governments imposed on the former Confederacy by the North. The actions of the Ku Klux Klan created additional pressure on the federal government to end the violence. People in the North also began to tire of efforts to change the South.

Directions: The cartoon on this page is from an 1872 newspaper. Study the cartoon, and then answer the questions that follow.

Culver Pictures, Inc.

(continued)

ANALYZING THE CARTOON

1. Who does the woman in the cartoon represent? How do you know this? Why is she shown in a bent-over posture?

   _____

   _____

2. What is the burden she is carrying?

   _____

   _____

3. What is the role of the two soldiers in the cartoon? Why is the woman chained to the rifles of the soldiers?

   _____

   _____

4. What details does the cartoonist include in the background to show the economic situation in the South?

   _____

   _____

CRITICAL THINKING

5. **Identifying Central Issues** What is the meaning of the words "Rule or Ruin" written on the paper tucked in among the bayonets?

   _____

   _____

   _____

6. **Determining Cause and Effect** How did interpretations such as the one shown here affect the outcome of the election of 1876?

   _____

   _____

   _____

7. **Evaluating Information** The cartoon on the previous page is from a Northern newspaper. What does its appearance in 1872 indicate about how Northern opinion had changed since 1865?

   _____

   _____

   _____

INTERPRETING POLITICAL CARTOONS

Activity 10

THOMAS NAST: AMERICA'S GREATEST POLITICAL CARTOONIST

Thomas Nast is considered the greatest American political cartoonist. Born in Germany, Nast came to the United States when he was six years old. When the Civil War broke out, Nast joined the staff of the pro-Union *Harper's Weekly.* His Civil War cartoons made him known throughout the country.

Nast became world famous for his cartoons after the war, especially those in which he attacked prejudice (see below and Activity 11) and political corruption (see Activities 12 and 13). Nast was an impassioned advocate for emancipation and the Union. Reconstruction brought another threat to African Americans, one that Nast opposed as vigorously as he did slavery.

Directions: Study the cartoon below and the excerpt from Shakespeare that accompanies it, and then answer the questions that follow.

"THESE FEW PRECEPTS IN THY MEMORY"

Beware of entrance to a quarrel:
  but, being in,
Bear it that the opposer may
  beware of thee.
Give every man thine ear, but
  few thy voice:
Take each man's censure, but
  reserve thy judgment.
Costly thy habit as thy purse
  can buy,
But not express'd in fancy;
  rich, not gaudy:
For the apparel oft proclaims
  the man.

• • • •

This above all,—To thine own
  self be true;
And it must follow, as the night
  the day,
Thou canst not then be false to
  any man.
  — SHAKESPEARE

"TO THINE OWN SELF BE TRUE."

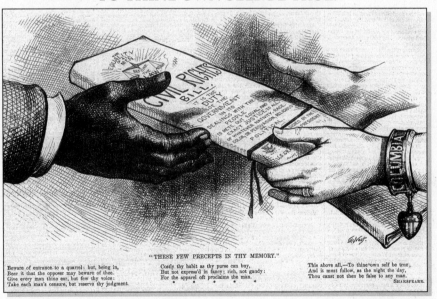

Harper's Weekly

(continued)

ANALYZING THE CARTOON

1. What is being handed to the African American?

   _____

   _____

2. Who is handing over the document in the cartoon? How do you
   know?

   _____

   _____

   _____

3. According to Nast, what is the duty of government that the Civil
   Rights Bill recognizes?

   _____

   _____

   _____

4. To what is Columbia married?

   _____

   _____

   _____

CRITICAL THINKING

5. **Drawing Conclusions** Nast quotes a famous speech from
   Shakespeare's *Hamlet,* in which a father (Polonius) gives advice to his
   son (Laertes) about how to live successfully and virtuously. The most
   famous lines are the final ones, beginning with "To thine own self be
   true." Explain Nast's use of these words as the cartoon's title and in
   the cartoon's caption.

   _____

   _____

   _____

6. **Making Inferences** What is the significance of Columbia presenting
   the document with two hands, rather than just one?

   _____

   _____

   _____

7. **Recognizing Bias** How might this cartoon have had a different slant if
   you could not see the African American's shirt sleeve and jacket?

   _____

   _____

   _____

INTERPRETING POLITICAL CARTOONS

NAST ON NATIVE AMERICANS

This cartoon was drawn after the uprising of the Santee Sioux in 1862. At that time, broken government promises and government apathy had left the Santee facing starvation. Mistrust was the order of the day between the Native Americans and settlers. An argument between two Santee men over eggs stolen from a white farmer turned into a dare to kill, and five settlers were killed. Anticipating retaliation from the army, the Santee rose up, killing about 450 settlers. United States troops mounted an overwhelming attack, and the Santee were subdued. Dozens were executed, existing treaties were voided, and the Santee were forcibly moved to South Dakota and then to Nebraska, where they remained.

Directions: Study the cartoon below, and then answer the questions that follow.

"MOVE ON"

HAS THE NATIVE AMERICAN NO RIGHTS THAT THE NATURALIZED AMERICAN IS BOUND TO RESPECT?

Library of Congress/*Harper's Weekly*

(continued)

ANALYZING THE CARTOON

1. How does Nast use caricature to indicate his feelings about the group of people in the background of the cartoon?

_____

_____

2. What is the meaning of the sign "The Polls" above the group of people in the background?

_____

_____

3. What is the meaning of the cartoon's caption, "Move On"? Who does the man in the middle represent?

_____

_____

4. What is Nast's point in the caption "Has the Native American no rights the naturalized American is bound to respect?"

_____

_____

CRITICAL THINKING

5. **Evaluating Information** Which character do you think is the central figure of the cartoon? How does Nast make your eyes focus on this person?

_____

_____

6. **Formulating Questions** What problems is Nast addressing in this cartoon? To determine the attitudes of the people toward these problems, make up one question you can ask each of the following: the people in the background, the man in the middle, and the man at the right. Then give what you think their answers would be to the question you have written.

_____

_____

7. **Making Predictions** From this cartoon and the cartoon in the previous activity, what would have been Nast's position during the civil rights struggles of the 1950s and the 1960s?

_____

_____

INTERPRETING POLITICAL CARTOONS

INTERPRETING POLITICAL CARTOONS

Activity 12

URBAN CORRUPTION

Perhaps the most dishonest of all politicians in the "Gilded Age" was William M. Tweed, called "Boss" Tweed. Tweed held various offices in New York City and New York State between 1851 and 1871. The most famous example of his dishonesty was the building of the "Tweed Courthouse" in New York City. During construction, Tweed ordered all contractors to add 100 percent to their bills and give the amount that was overcharged to the Tammany Ring. Under this system, New York City ended up paying $170,730 for 40 tables and chairs. When word began to reach the public, Thomas Nast drew the cartoon shown below for the *New York Times*.

Directions: Study the cartoon below, and then answer the questions that follow.

Library of Congress

(continued)

INTERPRETING POLITICAL CARTOONS

Name _____ Date _____ Class _____

ANALYZING THE CARTOON

1. What does the caption "Who Stole the People's Money?" suggest about the point of view of the cartoonist?

_____

_____

2. Which of the men is Boss Tweed? How does the cartoonist succeed in making him look ridiculous?

_____

_____

3. From the looks of the men in Tweed's circle, what classes of people appear to be part of the ring? How does the cartoonist show this?

_____

_____

_____

4. What do you think is Nast's opinion of the state of urban government at the time of Boss Tweed?

_____

_____

_____

CRITICAL THINKING

5. Understanding Cause and Effect What factors do you think allow some time periods to have greater political corruption than other time periods?

_____

_____

_____

6. Predicting Consequences What do you think are some of the most serious consequences of widespread corruption in government?

_____

_____

_____

INTERPRETING POLITICAL CARTOONS

Activity 13

INDUSTRIALIZATION AND URBAN POLITICS

Technological advances, immigration, and the prospects of wealth led to massive industrialization in the United States in the latter half of the 1800s and the early part of the 1900s. Industrialization led to the growth of cities, and cities often bred corrupt political organizations. The most famous of these was Tammany Hall in New York City. Its most famous leader was Boss Tweed, who railed against Thomas Nast's political cartoons, such as the one below. Nast waged an unrelenting campaign against Tammany corruption. Historians credit Nast's pressure with forcing the investigations that eventually brought down Boss Tweed.

Directions: Study the cartoon below, and then answer the questions that follow.

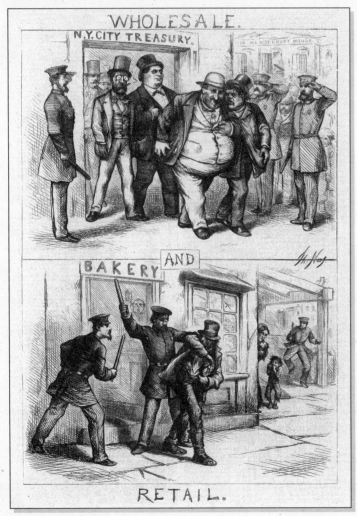

Harper's Weekly

(continued)

ANALYZING THE CARTOON

1. Name the central figure in the top panel of this cartoon. Who are the people with him?

   _____

   _____

2. Look at the central male figure in the bottom panel. From what economic class is he? Explain your answer.

   _____

   _____

3. What is the figure in the bottom panel doing? Why does Nast show him doing this?

   _____

   _____

4. Who is peeking around the corner in the bottom panel? Why is the child horrified?

   _____

   _____

5. What ironic, satirical pun is used in the cartoon's title?

   _____

   _____

CRITICAL THINKING

6. **Making Comparisons** Compare how the police are reacting in the bottom and top panels of this cartoon.

   _____

   _____

7. **Making Inferences** What have Boss Tweed and his cronies just done?

   _____

   _____

8. **Identifying Central Issues** Over the court house in the top right of the top panel, Nast wrote the following: "The New (?) Court House." Explain how the question mark after "New" expresses the central issue of this cartoon.

   _____

   _____

INTERPRETING POLITICAL CARTOONS

A NATION OF IMMIGRANTS: A CARTOONIST ON CHANGING TIMES

Joseph Keppler was a cartoonist for the magazine *Puck*. Keppler was the second-most famous cartoonist of his time, after Thomas Nast. Like Nast, Keppler immigrated to the United States. The issue of immigration, therefore, was close to his heart. Here are two views of immigration drawn by Keppler during different time periods. The top cartoon was drawn in the early 1880s, and the bottom cartoon was drawn in the 1890s.

Directions: Study the cartoons below, and then answer the questions that follow.

Library of Congress

"WELCOME TO ALL"

Culver Pictures, Inc.

(continued)

ANALYZING THE CARTOONS

1. In the top cartoon, who is the person on the left? How do you know? Who are the people facing him?

_____

_____

2. Who is greeting the immigrant in the bottom cartoon? How are they greeting him?

_____

_____

3. What do the shadows in the bottom cartoon's background symbolize?

_____

_____

CRITICAL THINKING

4. **Recognizing Bias** Stereotypes are exaggerations that make the false assumption that all members of a group have the same characteristics. These characteristics can be physical or part of behavior. How does this cartoonist use stereotypes?

_____

_____

5. **Identifying Central Issues** The title of the top cartoon is "Welcome to All." Write a title for the bottom cartoon.

_____

_____

6. **Making Inferences** What has happened between the first cartoon and the second cartoon that accounts for the difference in the portrayal and reception of the immigrants?

_____

_____

7. **Making Inferences** Do you think that Keppler's views about immigrants changed from the time he drew the first cartoon to the time he drew the second cartoon? Explain your answer.

_____

_____

_____

_____

INTERPRETING POLITICAL CARTOONS

Activity 15

BATTLE AGAINST THE TRUSTS

The growth of trusts in the oil refining, steel making, and other industries created huge problems for Americans. Trusts forced other companies out of business by using unfair methods. One method was to lower prices until other companies could not compete. Then, when there was no competition, the trusts would raise prices as high as they pleased. The trusts used their massive wealth to influence and interfere with government. As a result, more and more Americans came to believe that it was time for government to act against the trusts. This was a subject that many American cartoonists, including Joseph Keppler, dealt with around the beginning of the 1900s.

Directions: Study the cartoon below, and then answer the questions that follow.

Library of Congress

(continued)

ANALYZING THE CARTOON

1. What is the setting for this cartoon?

   _____

   _____

2. Who are the people in the front of the cartoon? Who are the people in the back row?

   _____

   _____

3. How does the cartoonist use size to make his point of view?

   _____

   _____

4. How does the cartoonist use caricature to make his point of view?

   _____

   _____

CRITICAL THINKING

5. **Synthesizing Information** Turn your attention to the sign at the top center of the cartoon. What does this sign mean? To what famous document in American history does the sign refer? How does the cartoonist use the sign to make an ironic point about the system of trusts?

   _____

   _____

   _____

6. **Analyzing Information** Note the closed door at the top left of the cartoon. What does it symbolize?

   _____

   _____

   _____

7. **Drawing Conclusions** What conclusions can you reach about the political preferences of the cartoonist? Is he attacking Republicans? Democrats? Both parties? Explain your answer.

   _____

   _____

   _____

INTERPRETING POLITICAL CARTOONS

A POPULIST VIEW OF PRESIDENT McKINLEY

The Sherman Antitrust Act was passed in 1890, but it was weak and did little to control trusts. Outrage over the trusts and their political influence grew, partly due to the work of muckraking journalists like Henry Demarest Lloyd. His antitrust book, *Wealth Against Commonwealth* (1894), influenced many people's thinking about regulation of the trusts. Populists were not heartened by the 1896 election of the pro-business William McKinley. The cartoons below—by Frederick Opper—show how, at this time, satire turned into sarcasm.

Directions: Study the cartoons below, and then answer the questions that follow.

"If Willie is a good boy, and minds papa and nursie, they will try to let him keep the pretty house until he is eight years old."

Library of Congress

"Yes, Willie, that was only one of the common people we ran over back there. He doesn't count."

(continued)

ANALYZING THE CARTOONS

1. Who is the nurse in the cartoons? What was his role in the politics of this time?

   _____

   _____

2. What makes the depictions of William McKinley and Teddy Roosevelt sarcastic?

   _____

   _____

3. What does Frederick Opper, the cartoonist, caricature in the Hanna figure, and what does it signify?

   _____

   _____

4. Explain the age reference in the caption of the left cartoon.

   _____

   _____

CRITICAL THINKING

5. **Making Inferences** What is Opper's view of McKinley's and Roosevelt's integrity?

   _____

   _____

6. **Recognizing Stereotypes** What stereotype is used with the figure representing the trusts? Is this a fair stereotype? Can a stereotype be fair?

   _____

   _____

7. **Making Comparisons** Who controlled politicians in the late 1800s, according to the muckrakers? What might we learn from the politics of the Gilded Age to help us deal with the role of money in the politics of our time?

   _____

   _____

8. **Making Predictions** What in these cartoons anticipates two major issues in the early twentieth century?

   _____

   _____

INTERPRETING POLITICAL CARTOONS

INTERPRETING POLITICAL CARTOONS

Activity 17

YELLOW JOURNALISM

There will always be controversy about the role that the sensationalistic, yellow journalism of William Randolph Hearst and Joseph Pulitzer played in instigating the Spanish-American War and, later, a fear of foreign invasion from Asia. We do know that the rise of yellow journalism coincided with an all-out competition between Hearst and Pulitzer for New York City's readership. The term "yellow journalism" originated from one of the first comic strips, "Yellow Kid," which Pulitzer published. Yellow was used for a color-production test at Pulitzer's *New York World*. Use of color was one of the sensationalistic methods of the day.

Directions: Study the cartoon below, and then answer the questions that follow.

Library of Congress

(continued)

ANALYZING THE CARTOON

1. How has the cartoonist used caricature in drawing the Japanese fisherman?

_____

_____

2. What is the mistake in the cartoon?

_____

_____

3. What is the origin of the term *yellow journalism?*

_____

_____

4. What is the fisherman using for a pole and for bait?

_____

_____

_____

5. What does Uncle Sam mean when he refers to the land being "posted"? What is it that posts the land?

_____

_____

_____

CRITICAL THINKING

6. **Summarizing Information** What was the essential message of the Monroe Doctrine?

_____

_____

_____

7. **Synthesizing Information** Thomas Powers, one of the cartoonists Hearst recruited during the circulation war with Pulitzer, drew this cartoon. How is the cartoon an example of Hearst-style, yellow journalism?

_____

_____

_____

INTERPRETING POLITICAL CARTOONS

Activity 18

BIG STICK DIPLOMACY IN THE WESTERN HEMISPHERE

Theodore Roosevelt threw his considerable energy into building United States authority in Latin America. He established policies that would affect United States relations with Latin America throughout the 1900s. Roosevelt's "big stick" policy expressed the view that it was the responsibility of the United States to carry out "the most regrettable but necessary international police duty which must be performed for the sake of the welfare of mankind." When Venezuela defaulted on loans in 1902, Roosevelt warned against European intervention in the Western Hemisphere. He persuaded the parties to submit the dispute to arbitration.

Directions: The new United States policy in Latin America stirred considerable controversy. The cartoon below appeared after the Venezuela intervention. Study the cartoon, and then answer the questions that follow.

Library of Congress

(continued)

ANALYZING THE CARTOON

1. What is the meaning of the paper tucked under Roosevelt's left arm marked "arbitration"?

   _____

   _____

2. Why does the nightstick have the words "The New Diplomacy" printed on it?

   _____

   _____

3. What building is shown under Roosevelt's right arm? Why is it there?

   _____

   _____

CRITICAL THINKING

4. **Synthesizing Information** What famous Roosevelt saying is represented in this cartoon? Explain your answer.

   _____

   _____

5. **Recognizing Bias** How does the cartoonist use stereotypes to state his message? What groups are stereotyped?

   _____

   _____

6. **Analyzing Information** Look at the land the characters in the cartoon are standing on. How does the cartoonist manipulate geography to make his point of view?

   _____

   _____

7. **Drawing Conclusions** Is the cartoon supportive or critical of Theodore Roosevelt? Explain your answer.

   _____

   _____

   _____

INTERPRETING POLITICAL CARTOONS   Activity 19

WOMEN CAMPAIGN FOR SUFFRAGE

Most political cartoonists have been male. The campaign to win the vote for women created a number of magazines, journals, and newspapers, however, and women often were hired as political cartoonists for these outlets. Some of the well-known female cartoonists for suffrage were Nina Allender, Lou Rogers, Laura Foster, and Edwina Dumm. Ironically, when the Nineteenth Amendment was ratified in 1920, many female cartoonists lost their jobs because much of the media supporting the cause shut down. The Lou Rogers cartoon below uses the figure of Mrs. Sam, wife to Uncle Sam. A number of suffrage cartoonists gave Uncle Sam a wife, who challenged her husband to live up to what he symbolized.

Directions: Study the cartoon below, and then answer the questions that follow.

Lou Rogers in the Woman Citizen

Mrs. Sam: "It is Terribly Humiliating to Me, Sam, to Have You Go to Europe in Last Century's Hat."

Culver Pictures, Inc.

(continued)

ANALYZING THE CARTOON

1. What symbols help identify the male figure as Uncle Sam?

   _____

   _____

2. What is Uncle Sam's reason for going to Europe? How do you know?

   _____

   _____

3. From Rogers's drawing, what kind of woman do you think Mrs. Sam is? Why do you think this? How does this image fit with the arguments mainstream suffragists were making to gain the vote for women?

   _____

   _____

4. What about the "hat" in the cartoon refers to the basic reason for the American Revolution?

   _____

   _____

CRITICAL THINKING

5. **Making Inferences** How does the caption turn a "typical woman's" worry into an ironic statement on the "modernization" of the United States?

   _____

   _____

   _____

6. **Drawing Conclusions** From the facial expression of Uncle Sam, what is Lou Rogers's view of how well America is responding to women's demands for the vote?

   _____

   _____

   _____

7. **Formulating Questions** What do you think Lou Rogers would ask an employer who refused to hire a female political cartoonist?

   _____

   _____

   _____

INTERPRETING POLITICAL CARTOONS

A LEAGUE NOT OF OUR OWN

Renewed isolationism and Republican opposition led by Senator Henry Cabot Lodge of Massachusetts spelled defeat for the Versailles Treaty in the U.S. Congress. American inclusion in the League of Nations died with it. The irony that the United States joined Germany as the two Western powers not in the League did not escape President Wilson during his speaking tour to drum up support for passage of the treaty. Wilson was not successful, however, and the Senate voted twice against ratification. The final blow came in President Harding's 1920 inaugural address when, in reference to the famous Farewell Address of President Washington, he announced that the United States would not be entangled in European affairs.

Directions: Study the cartoon below, and then answer the questions that follow.

"WE TOLD YOU IT WOULDN'T WORK!"

Courtesy of the J.N. "Ding" Darling Foundation.

(continued)

ANALYZING THE CARTOON

1. What kind of truck has its wheel off? What pictorial evidence tells you it is this kind of truck?

_____

_____

_____

2. Who is the figure sitting on the wheel? How do you know? What is his attitude toward the League?

_____

_____

_____

3. What is the attitude of the crowd of men on the right side of the cartoon?

_____

_____

_____

4. What is the fire that the League of Nations is being called to put out?

_____

_____

_____

CRITICAL THINKING

5. **Identifying Point of View** This cartoon was drawn by Jay Darling, who worked under the name "Ding." What is Ding's point of view toward the U.S. position on the League of Nations? Be sure to support your answer with evidence from the cartoon.

_____

_____

_____

6. **Drawing Conclusions** According to the cartoon, what is the effect of the United States's non-participation in the League of Nations? Explain your answer.

_____

_____

_____

INTERPRETING POLITICAL CARTOONS

THE GATES TO IMMIGRATION CLOSE

During World War I, there was a rise in antiforeign feelings among Americans. All over the country, for example, German street names were replaced with non-German names. After the war, a new flood of immigrants entered the country, and antiforeign feelings rose to a fever pitch. Workers worried that immigrants would compete for jobs and, because they would work for lower wages, drive down wages. Many feared that a wave of communism would spread over the land. As a result, many Americans grew suspicious of people who were "different." During the 1920s, the United States government passed a series of laws restricting immigration. These new laws established a quota system, which limited the number of immigrants entering the United States.

Directions: The cartoon on this page represents the feelings of millions of Americans as the decade of the 1920s got underway. Study the cartoon, and then answer the questions that follow.

Library of Congress

(continued)

ANALYZING THE CARTOON

1. Who is the main character in the cartoon? What is he doing?

_____

_____

_____

2. Who are the people on shore? Why are they happy?

_____

_____

_____

3. How does the cartoonist use stereotyping and caricature to show his opposition to immigration?

_____

_____

_____

CRITICAL THINKING

4. **Drawing Conclusions** What factors mentioned in the introduction to this activity have led to anti-immigrant feelings in the United States in recent years? What factors behind opposition to immigration today are not mentioned in the introduction?

_____

_____

_____

5. **Making Predictions** What kind of impact do you think such a cartoon would have today?

_____

_____

_____

6. **Making Generalizations** Do you think there was an outcry when this cartoon appeared in a newspaper in the 1920s? Why was it acceptable then and would not be acceptable today?

_____

_____

_____

INTERPRETING POLITICAL CARTOONS

Activity 22

NATIVE AMERICANS AND A NATION OF IMMIGRANTS

At times throughout its history, the United States has welcomed people from foreign lands, and at times it has shunned them. In the 1900s, as new waves of immigrants reached the United States, there was increasing opposition to immigration. This political cartoonist takes many opportunities to use satire to comment on the situation. The long presence of Native Americans in the Americas was one element of that satire.

Directions: Study the cartoon below, and then answer the questions that follow.

Steve Kelley © 1994 *San Diego Union Tribune*, Copley News Service.

(continued)

ANALYZING THE CARTOON

1. Who are the people grouped on the left of the cartoon?

_____

_____

2. What is the meaning of the comment made by the person on the right?

_____

_____

3. In the cartoon, the artist uses many devices to convey the emotions of his message. Answer the following questions about each person or group of people pictured in the cartoon: (a) What are the emotions of the person or people? (b) How does the cartoonist show this?

	Emotions	How Shown
A. Group of three people on the left		
B. Person in middle		
C. Person on right		

CRITICAL THINKING

4. **Analyzing Information** One of the ways cartoonists use humor to send their messages is through the use of irony. Irony is a statement that is obviously the opposite of reality. How is irony used in this cartoon?

_____

_____

5. **Drawing Conclusions** What are the factors that have led to anti-immigrant feelings in the United States in recent years?

_____

_____

6. **Synthesizing Information** Create a new set of ironic statements by the characters. Use any or all of the people shown in the cartoon.

_____

_____

_____

INTERPRETING POLITICAL CARTOONS

INTERPRETING POLITICAL CARTOONS

Activity 23

THE GREAT DEPRESSION

By 1932—three years after the crash of the stock market—almost half of the banks in the United States had failed, unemployment was nearing 30 percent, and stocks had fallen to about 20 percent of their pre-crash value. It may seem that such a situation was no laughing matter and that political cartooning would, therefore, decline. As the following cartoon shows, however, people still found a way to satirize events even when conditions were at their worst.

Directions: Study the cartoon below, and then answer the questions that follow.

A WISE ECONOMIST ASKS A QUESTION

(continued)

ANALYZING THE CARTOON

1. What does the man on the park bench represent?

_____

_____

_____

2. What does the location of the man (sitting on a park bench) add to the cartoon?

_____

_____

_____

3. How is the man caricatured to show that he is a responsible citizen?

_____

_____

_____

CRITICAL THINKING

4. **Understanding Symbolism** What does the squirrel symbolize? Why is the squirrel a good symbol for this?

_____

_____

_____

5. **Understanding Cause and Effect** What were the causes of the Great Depression?

_____

_____

_____

6. **Synthesizing Information** What short-term and long-term measures did President Franklin Roosevelt take to handle the rash of bank failures?

_____

_____

_____

_____

INTERPRETING POLITICAL CARTOONS

Activity 24

THE NEW DEAL

Franklin Roosevelt's New Deal had three main goals in response to the Great Depression: to provide immediate help to millions of Americans, to improve the economy, and to reform laws that favored the rich and powerful over the poor and the powerless. These goals were dubbed the "Three Rs:" relief, recovery, and reform. Historians consider the New Deal one of the most important events in American history. At the time, however, many Americans were skeptical or critical of the tactics and policies of the New Deal. Here are two cartoons that raise questions about it. Both were drawn in 1935.

Directions: Study the cartoons, and then answer the questions that follow.

TROJAN HORSE AT OUR GATE

Library of Congress

(continued)

ANALYZING THE CARTOONS

1. Explain the horse in the top cartoon.

   _____

   _____

2. In the top cartoon, what is the gate to the city? Who is guarding the
   city?

   _____

   _____

3. What New Deal programs or legislation might the cartoonist of the top
   cartoon think were not constitutional?

   _____

   _____

4. In the bottom cartoon, what does the hat of the person in the rear tell
   you about his work?

   _____

   _____

CRITICAL THINKING

5. **Analyzing Information** In the bottom cartoon, look at the person
   holding the mask and the person holding the document that reads
   "Redistribution of Wealth" What pieces of caricature has the cartoonist
   used to identify them as certain types?

   _____

   _____

6. **Making Comparisons** Compare the smile on the mask and of the men
   in the bottom cartoon. What is different about them?

   _____

   _____

7. **Making Generalizations** What point do both cartoons make about
   those behind the New Deal?

   _____

   _____

8. **Identifying Point of View** What is the point of view of the bottom
   cartoonist about the New Deal?

   _____

   _____

INTERPRETING POLITICAL CARTOONS

WORLD WAR II

The Allies defeated the Germans and Italians in North Africa and then invaded Italy. At this point, the war was beginning to favor the Allies, and the Axis war machine no longer seemed invincible. This cartoon captures that spirit of the Allies being in control. Indeed, after defeating the Germans and Italians in North Africa, the Allies worked their way north through Italy and entered Rome on D-Day.

Directions: Study the cartoon, and then answer the questions that follow.

"WHO'S NEXT"

Courtesy of the J.N. "Ding" Darling Foundation.

(continued)

ANALYZING THE CARTOON

1. Who are the three men on the left? Who are the three men in the upper right-hand corner?

   _____

   _____

2. What about going into surgery fits the reaction of the future "patients"? What are the signs of their reaction?

   _____

   _____

3. From what army is the soldier who is being wheeled out? What two things tell you that? What has happened to him?

   _____

   _____

4. What caricature does the cartoonist use to identify Stalin? Mussolini? Tojo?

   _____

   _____

CRITICAL THINKING

5. **Analyzing Information** The cartoon is entitled "Who's Next." We know that Italy was next. What indicates this fact in the cartoon?

   _____

   _____

6. **Making Inferences** Look at Stalin's and Churchill's facial expressions. What mood does each indicate?

   _____

   _____

7. **Synthesizing Information** Note the sign "Operating Room" and the paper nailed to the doorframe, which says "Major Operation Schedule." What ironic pun is the cartoonist using here?

   _____

   _____

8. **Drawing Conclusions** Why is Hitler larger than the Italian and Japanese leaders?

   _____

   _____

INTERPRETING POLITICAL CARTOONS

JOSEPH McCARTHY AND THE RED SCARE

Senator Joseph McCarthy seized on Americans' fears about communism to become the most controversial and infamous American of his time. McCarthy made sensational claims about Communist penetration of the United States government, and he accused many people of being Communist agents. One of the Americans most offended by McCarthy was the cartoonist Herbert Block, who drew under the name Herblock. Herblock was one of the most famous American political cartoonists of the 1900s. He drew his satirical cartoons for more than 60 years, principally at the *Washington Post*.

Directions: Study the cartoon below, and then answer the questions that follow.

From Herblock's *Here and Now*, Simon & Schuster, 1955.

(continued)

ANALYZING THE CARTOON

1. Who is the person in the cartoon?

   _____

   _____

2. What is the meaning of the term "doctored photo"?

   _____

   _____

3. How does the cartoonist use caricature to make a point about
   McCarthy?

   _____

   _____

   _____

4. Explain the title of the cartoon.

   _____

   _____

   _____

CRITICAL THINKING

5. **Identifying the Main Idea** What is the main point of the cartoon?
   Explain how Herblock uses irony to make this main point.

   _____

   _____

   _____

6. **Recognizing Stereotypes** How does the cartoonist use stereotypes to
   make a point about McCarthy's character, and what is that point?

   _____

   _____

   _____

7. **Determining Cause and Effect** What impact do you think the
   McCarthy Era has had on the values of Americans today?

   _____

   _____

   _____

INTERPRETING POLITICAL CARTOONS

Activity 27

THE DEATH OF JFK

A well-known saying is "A picture is worth a thousand words." Few images confirm this idea as well as Bill Mauldin's response to the assassination of President Kennedy. Some cartoons convey their messages through a single gesture or pose. The action's simplicity can touch the viewer deeply. In this cartoon, Mauldin expressed the national response to Kennedy's assassination. For the moment, shared shock and grief set aside political differences as everyone mourned.

Directions: Study the cartoon below, and then answer the questions that follow.

(continued)

ANALYZING THE CARTOON

1. What statue has Mauldin drawn?

_____

_____

2. Where is this statue located? What does the location add to the power of the cartoon?

_____

_____

3. What is the character in the cartoon doing? How do you know? What does Mauldin want to convey through this action?

_____

_____

4. What does the shadow on the wall on the right side of the cartoon symbolize?

_____

_____

CRITICAL THINKING

5. **Determining Cause and Effect** What is the effect of having a statue come to life?

_____

_____

_____

6. **Analyzing Information** Consider the important national events of President Kennedy's presidency. What does Mauldin convey about the loss of Kennedy by associating him with Abraham Lincoln?

_____

_____

_____

7. **Drawing Conclusions** This cartoon has no dialogue, commentary, caption, or title. What are the effects of this silence on the viewer?

_____

_____

_____

INTERPRETING POLITICAL CARTOONS

INTERPRETING POLITICAL CARTOONS

VIETNAM

The involvement of the United States in the Vietnam War divided the country. Many political, economic, and philosophical matters were at issue. Through the rhetoric of all the controversy, this cartoon picked out the most compelling matter: the people in Vietnam for whom, supposedly, the war was being fought, who suffered the most from it, and who had the hardest time understanding it. This cartoon appeared on January 14, 1965.

Directions: Study the cartoon, and then answer the questions that follow.

"Who's winning—the forces of freedom or the people's democracies?"

(continued)

ANALYZING THE CARTOON

1. Which side of the war were the "forces of freedom" and which side were the "people's democracies"? Why are these two names almost equivalent?

_____

_____

2. What is the situation of the family in the cartoon?

_____

_____

3. What clues tell you that the war depicted in this cartoon is the Vietnam War?

_____

_____

4. What is the effect of putting children in this cartoon?

_____

_____

CRITICAL THINKING

5. **Making Generalizations** Look at the cartoon from Activity 1. Do the two cartoons make the same point? Why or why not?

_____

_____

_____

6. **Making Comparisons** What is similar about how this cartoon and the cartoon in Activity 1 make their points?

_____

_____

_____

7. **Identifying Point of View** From what point of view is each of these cartoons drawn?

_____

_____

_____

INTERPRETING POLITICAL CARTOONS

INTERPRETING POLITICAL CARTOONS

Activity 29

NIXON ON CIVIL RIGHTS

During the Nixon administration (1969–1974), there were mixed messages regarding civil rights. In 1971 the Supreme Court sanctioned the controversial step of busing school children to achieve racial balance and integration. In addition, in 1970 the Voting Rights Amendment Act put a five-year ban on literacy requirements for voting. The ban became permanent in 1975.

Nixon's actions as president, however, showed little sensitivity to the cause of African Americans or other minorities. Cuts in aid to the poor and the seeming indifference to discrimination in hiring practices were just a few examples of this insensitivity.

Directions: Study the cartoon below, and then answer the questions that follow.

"By th' way, what's that big word?"

Copyright © 1962 by Bill Mauldin. Reprinted with permission of Bill Mauldin.

(continued)

ANALYZING THE CARTOON

1. Who are the two people shown in the cartoon?

   _____

   _____

   _____

2. What is a literacy test?

   _____

   _____

   _____

3. Explain the irony in the cartoon.

   _____

   _____

   _____

4. How does the cartoonist use caricature to show bias?

   _____

   _____

   _____

CRITICAL THINKING

5. **Determining Cause and Effect** How did having to pass a literacy test affect voting rights?

   _____

   _____

   _____

6. **Identifying Central Issues** What is the basic issue on which the cartoonist is focusing?

   _____

   _____

   _____

INTERPRETING POLITICAL CARTOONS

Activity 30

ACHIEVING EQUALITY FOR WOMEN

In modern times, the Founders of our nation have come under criticism for stating too vaguely the way in which equality would take root in the new nation. Specifically, the rights of women were largely not discussed in the Constitution. Not until the woman suffrage movement of the early 1900s did women begin to assert basic freedoms that white men had exercised since the founding of the nation. In recent years, many issues—including those in the proposed Equal Rights Amendment and the "equal pay for equal work" concern—remind us that the equality of women has not yet been realized. The cartoon below illustrates the cartoonist's view of the neglect of the Founders with respect to women's issues.

Directions: Study the cartoon, and then answer the questions that follow.

Mike Peters, reprinted by permission of UFS, Inc.

(continued)

ANALYZING THE CARTOON

1. Who are the men in the cartoon?

_____

_____

_____

2. From what document are the men reading?

_____

_____

_____

3. What does the woman scrubbing the floor symbolize?

_____

_____

_____

CRITICAL THINKING

4. Making Generalizations Do you see any problems in the document's wording, "All men are created equal"? Explain.

_____

_____

_____

5. Analyzing Information Explain the irony in the statement, "That's beautiful Tom."

_____

_____

_____

6. Demonstrating Reasoned Judgment Do you think there should be an amendment to the Constitution that specifically states women's rights? Explain your response.

_____

_____

_____

INTERPRETING POLITICAL CARTOONS

Activity 31

QUESTIONING CULTURAL VALUES

   Henry Ford once stated that he invented the automobile so people could drive out from the city on the weekend and enjoy the wide open spaces. As the cartoon shows, the problem with Ford's statement was he never anticipated that roads, cars, and people would fill those spaces.

Directions: Study the cartoon below, and then answer the questions that follow.

(continued)

ANALYZING THE CARTOON

1. What American historical references are in the slogan, "Trail-Blaze a New Destiny"?

_____

2. What is the meaning of the question on the billboard?

_____

3. Why does the cartoonist name the car "Fire Storm"?

_____

_____

4. Where has the driver been? How do you know? What point is the cartoonist making about where she has been?

_____

_____

5. To what does "Mach 8" refer?

_____

_____

CRITICAL THINKING

6. **Making Comparisons** What recent or current car names now refer to the Old West?

_____

_____

7. **Drawing Conclusions** What about advertising does this cartoon expose?

_____

_____

8. **Making Inferences** Do you think the cartoonist is liberal or conservative? Explain your answer.

_____

_____

9. **Synthesizing Information** Write an advertisement for an automobile. Include references to aspects of American identity, gender, or both.

_____

_____

INTERPRETING POLITICAL CARTOONS

PIERCING THE REAGAN DOCTRINE

President Reagan's firm anti-Communist stance led him to support movements within foreign countries to prop up or install governments sympathetic to America, but not necessarily in touch with their citizens. Similar attempts by other U.S. administrations often had not worked well in the past. However, the practice of direct or covert support was especially popular among those who criticized containment as an anti-Communist policy.

Directions: Study the cartoon below, looking especially for references to past attempts to control or create foreign governments. Then answer the questions that follow.

(continued)

ANALYZING THE CARTOON

1. Who is Westmoreland? What provides graphic clues to his identity?
   Why was he picked for the cartoon?

   _____

   _____

2. Who are the Sandinistas?

   _____

   _____

3. Who is the man on the horse? How would you describe his expression? What is this expression supposed to tell us?

   _____

   _____

4. What words in the cartoon refer to the American involvement in Vietnam?

   _____

CRITICAL THINKING

5. **Analyzing Information** Pat Oliphant, the cartoonist, always put one or more talking birds in the bottom of his cartoons. What is their function?

   _____

   _____

6. **Recognizing Stereotypes** Look at the figure to Westmoreland's left. What is he and how is he stereotyped? What can you infer about Oliphant's point of view toward him from how he is drawn?

   _____

   _____

7. **Drawing Conclusions** What historical reference does President Reagan make when responding to Westmoreland? What evidence makes you come to your conclusion? What else about Reagan refers to this same period? Why does Oliphant make this reference?

   _____

   _____

8. **Identifying Central Issues** Create a title for this cartoon that expresses the main issue to which it relates.

   _____

   _____

INTERPRETING POLITICAL CARTOONS

INTERPRETING POLITICAL CARTOONS Activity 33

ENVIRONMENTAL AWARENESS

The 1980s brought a new societal awareness of environmental issues and concerns. Scientists and environmental advocates published dramatic findings showing that the habits of Americans—from individuals in their homes to industrial corporations—were harming our environment and threatening our planet. Today our habits are slowly changing, but there are still many environmental issues upon which to focus, such as ever-expanding landfills and emissions harmful to the atmosphere.

Directions: Study the cartoon below, and then answer the questions that follow.

BEFORE IT WAS TRENDY TO BE SENSITIVE TO OUR ENVIRONMENT THERE WAS ONE GROUP OF AMERICANS...

...WHO BELIEVED THE EARTH WAS A LIVING BEING DESERVING TO BE TREATED WITH CARE AND RESPECT.

WE CALLED THEM SAVAGES

WICKS
© THE SIGNAL 1990

© Randy Wicks/*The Signal*.

(continued)

ANALYZING THE CARTOON

1. Is this cartoon primarily addressing our ignorance toward the environment or the way in which Native Americans have been treated?

_____

_____

_____

2. How does this cartoonist seem to feel about the current American interest in protecting the environment?

_____

_____

_____

3. What is the irony in the cartoon?

_____

_____

_____

4. Why do you think the cartoonist chose not to illustrate the cartoon more fully?

_____

_____

_____

CRITICAL THINKING

5. **Identifying Assumptions** Why do you think Americans seem to have taken the environment for granted, allowing these problems to develop?

_____

_____

_____

6. **Recognizing Stereotypes** Look at the Native American figure. How is he stereotyped? Do you think this stereotype helps or hinders the message of the cartoon? Explain your response.

_____

_____

_____

INTERPRETING POLITICAL CARTOONS

Activity 34

THIRD PARTIES

Beginning with the Federalists and Anti-Federalists, and solidified by the Democrats and Republicans, America has always had a two-party system. Nonetheless, American history is full of attempts to organize and maintain other parties, such as the Progressive Party, which nominated Teddy Roosevelt in 1912; the Socialist Party, for which Eugene Debs garnered over 900,000 votes in 1920; and the States' Rights Party, which nominated Strom Thurmond for president in 1948. Critics of the two-party system typically argue that there is no real difference between the two parties because each leans to the center and each is in the pockets of powerful special interests. The 1990s saw a third party—the Reform Party—rise to national prominence when Ross Perot received 19 percent of the popular vote in the 1992 presidential election.

Directions: Study the cartoon below, and then answer the questions that follow.

"Each candidate will be allowed an opening sound-bite, then they may respond to questions with a memorable slogan or withering put-down, and finally have the chance for a closing zinger..."

(continued)

ANALYZING THE CARTOON

1. Who are the candidates, from left to right?

   _____

   _____

   _____

2. What aspect of the cartoon tells the reader that the debate should not
   be taken seriously?

   _____

   _____

   _____

3. According to the "debate rules," what two things will candidates try
   to do?

   _____

   _____

   _____

CRITICAL THINKING

4. **Categorizing Information** To which political party does each candidate in the cartoon belong?

   _____

   _____

   _____

5. **Making Inferences** From this cartoon, what can you infer about
   Americans' expectations of televised presidential debates?

   _____

   _____

   _____

6. **Drawing Conclusions** Why does television tend to reduce the candidates' messages to sound-bites and slogans?

   _____

   _____

   _____

INTERPRETING POLITICAL CARTOONS

INTERPRETING POLITICAL CARTOONS

Activity 35

THE DECLINE OF COMMUNISM

During the 1990s, the world watched closely as the Communist leaders of Eastern Europe failed to bring their countries out of economic confusion and political chaos. Beginning with the dramatic rejection of Communist rule in East Germany, other Soviet satellite countries did the same. The peoples of the former Soviet Republics, such as Moldova, Estonia, and Lithuania, have opted for independence from central Communist rule to try to rebuild their governments in the likeness of Western democracy. One of the few surviving hard-line Communist governments exists in Cuba under Fidel Castro. Even after losing subsidies from former Communist allies, Castro's regime has held on.

Directions: Study the cartoon below, and then answer the questions that follow.

© 1990 Dave Granlund.

(continued)

INTERPRETING POLITICAL CARTOONS

ANALYZING THE CARTOON

1. Who is the person in the cartoon?

_____

_____

2. What is the person doing?

_____

_____

3. Describe some elements of this cartoon that make it humorous.

_____

_____

4. What is the cartoon saying about communism?

_____

_____

CRITICAL THINKING

5. **Summarizing Information** What are some of the countries whose leaders would have been present at this reunion in 1985?

_____

_____

_____

6. **Identifying Alternatives** What factors might impact Castro's government and force it to undergo basic change?

_____

_____

_____

7. **Identifying the Main Idea** Write a title that expresses the main point of this cartoon. Explain your choice.

_____

_____

_____

INTERPRETING POLITICAL CARTOONS

Activity 36

APATHY AMONG AMERICAN VOTERS

The history of the United States is based on democracy. Democracy, in turn, is founded upon the idea that supreme authority rests with the people, who express their opinions and desires primarily through voting. Low voter turnout in recent elections, however, seems to signal a state of apathy, or lack of interest, among voters. In addition, fewer and fewer citizens take part in such political activities as volunteering for campaigns.

Directions: Study the cartoon below, and then answer the questions that follow.

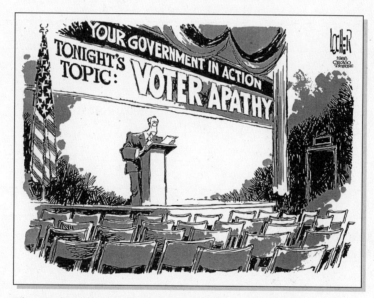

Tribune Media Services, Inc. All rights reserved. Reprinted with permission.

(continued)

ANALYZING THE CARTOON

1. What is the biggest symbol of apathy in the cartoon?

_____

_____

_____

2. Why is the symbol of apathy effective?

_____

_____

_____

3. What view is the cartoonist expressing about the state of voter interest in the United States?

_____

_____

_____

CRITICAL THINKING

4. **Making Predictions** What impact might a lack of voter interest and participation have on the democratic process?

_____

_____

_____

5. **Identifying Cause-and-Effect Relationships** What do you think are some of the causes of apathy in American voters?

_____

_____

_____

6. **Identifying the Main Idea** Write a title that expresses the main point of this cartoon. Explain your choice.

_____

_____

_____

Political Cartoon 1

1. The cartoonist seems to view the battle as foolish. He favors neither side, treating each as anonymous, identical forces that mirror each other.

2. The people appear to be confused about the battle and detached from it. They are not concerned about who will win.

3. The people have apathetic postures and uncomprehending expressions. Along with italicizing the word "our" in the caption, the postures and expressions indicate the people's lack of interest and confusion.

4. Answers will vary but should include the exaggeration of the equally herd-like armies rushing toward each other and the fact that they are identical.

5. Answers will vary but might refer to any conflict that was sold to the public as a heroic enterprise but later did not meet that expectation.

6. Answers will vary but make sure the cartoons are satirical in the sense that they use exaggerated humor to make an appropriate point.

Political Cartoon 2

1. The heroic, conquering stance of Columbus; the way he is the focus of the picture; and the armor, cross, and Spanish flags all show this event is very important.

2. The cartoonist copies the composition of the engraving. All the main characters have the same poses, flags are in the same positions, and the trees are in the same position.

3. The people who have landed are space aliens. The cartoonist uses them because of the modern fascination with extraterrestrials and UFOs.

4. People are cowering and running in fear. The cartoonist is pointing out that we have a different perspective on events when they happen to us; and that because we know

the results of Columbus's landing and how it affected Native Americans, we understand what the aliens intend to do.

5. The cartoonist is not commenting on Columbus, but rather on how people have interpreted Columbus. The main point is that historical events look different when they are not serving one's interests. We should rethink the landing of Columbus with this idea in mind.

6. Answers will vary, but students should explain how the cartoonists have expressed their points of view.

Political Cartoon 3

1. The letters stand for the colonies and colonial groupings.

2. The New England colonies are grouped together under the label "N.E." and Georgia is not included.

3. In unity there is strength. (a.)

4. The message was that the colonies could not survive unless they collaborated more closely.

5. Answers will vary. On the affirmative side, national unity is important in an age of racial discord. On the negative side, the idea of a strong national government is overwhelmingly accepted by Americans today, and the relevancy of Franklin's message is not needed because it is generally accepted.

6. Answers will vary, but students should include the concept that there is strength in unity.

7. Answers will vary, but the discussion of symbolism will give the students a better insight into the mind of a cartoonist.

Political Cartoon 4

1. A mercenary is a professional soldier who fights for hire without regard for political or patriotic allegiance. The more than 15,000 German Hessians who fought for

the British are the most well-known mercenaries of the American Revolution. Some argue that in this case the term is misleading, however, because the Hessians were part of the German army, they were paid much lower wages than most mercenaries of the time, and rarely joined the rebellious colonists when offered higher pay.

2. The man peering out the window belongs to the upper classes. We know this from his ruffled collar and white (powdered) wig.

3. The best sign of their low rank is the fact that even though it is winter, their feet are wrapped in strips of cloth. They have no shoes or boots.

4. The ironic joke in the caption tells us that they are being paid very little for their service.

5. A sunshine patriot is someone who is loyal only when the going is easy (the weather is good). The man peering out the window in the bottom cartoon is a sunshine patriot. He displays the flag of whoever is in power.

6. The winter setting, the low pay, and the lack of shoes in the left cartoon all tell us that these were drawn to commemorate Valley Forge.

Political Cartoon 5

1. The turtle represents the Embargo Act.

2. The man with the barrel is a smuggler trying to smuggle cargo to the waiting ship.

3. The Union Jack on the ship's stern tells us it is British. It is waiting to take on the smuggled cargo.

4. The key to the meaning is understanding that "ograbme" is "embargo" spelled backwards. The word refers to the Embargo Act and the pun is that the turtle (the Act) is grabbing the smuggler in its mouth.

5. The cartoonist is in favor of the act. The evidence is that the smuggler is drawn unfavorably, while the other man is not.

6. Answers will vary. Some possibilities: "Bar me," "O bar me," "mob rage," and "Go rob me."

7. The effectiveness of the Embargo Act is questionable, because it stirred up domestic ferment and hurt the United States. Further, the United States ultimately was not able to maintain its neutrality. Answers will vary. Make sure answers are supported by facts and reasons.

Political Cartoon 6

1. The cartoonists are against gerrymandering. In the left cartoon, the wings, expression, flicking serpent's tongue, and talons make the beast a bird of prey, a gargoyle, or a dragon. The frightening creature appears to be evil and destructive. The message seems to be that gerrymandering threatens a democratic system. In the right cartoon, the cartoonist has used satire to point out the absurdity of gerrymandering.

2. A congressional district is compared to an abstract, unrealistic painting.

3. One reason is that the sharp contrast between black and white makes it easier for the viewer to see the gerrymandering, but the cartoonist may also intend a reference to the districts being redrawn along racial lines.

4. The title is a satirical reference to the lack of realism in the redistricting.

5. Answers will vary. Some students might argue that such districting would help ensure solidarity and enhance power for a minority group. Students against such districting might argue that it would give too much power to a majority racial or ethnic group. Check for a reasoned expression of whatever view is given.

6. Answers will vary. Considerations could include that (a) the frightening nature of the left cartoon makes it more effective by showing the threat of gerrymandering; or (b) the fact that portions of the districts

in the right cartoon are entirely discon-
nected make it more effective by showing
the absurdity of gerrymandering.

7. The term comes from the last name of the
Governor of Massachusetts who spear-
headed and benefited from the redistricting,
and the fact that the redrawn districts
reminded Tilsdale of a salamander on its
side.

8. The Fifteenth Amendment bars infringe-
ment to vote based on race, color, or previous slavery. Districting can infringe on this
right. Gerrymandering can ensure that a
party's candidate does not get elected by
dividing the party members between or
among districts. In the same way, it can
also guarantee that a party's candidate
does get elected.

Political Cartoon 7

1. The bottom cartoon shows him driving
evil bankers out of the bank to support the
common people. The top cartoon shows
him as a king, stomping on the United
States Constitution to get his way.

2. Jackson is shown much larger than the
people the cartoon opposes—the bankers
of the Second Bank of the United States.
Other symbols: the pillars of the bank
crumbling; a "devil" as a banker, bankers
as robbers leaving the bank with bags of
money.

3. Jackson is shown as a monarch with cape,
crown, scepter, and throne. He holds a
sheet of paper marked "veto." He tramples
on the Constitution of the United States.

4. Because there were people alive at the time
who had fought in the American Revolution
(Jackson being one), Americans would be
much more sensitive to the charge that an
elected leader was trying to impose dicta-
torial rule.

5. One can infer that the pro-Jackson cartoon
was more popular in the West and among
farmers, and that the anti-Jackson cartoon

was more popular in the East and among
lawyers.

6. Selected cartoons will vary. Cartoons
should show pro and con attitudes toward
the same person.

Political Cartoon 8

1. The cartoonist has written "North" and
"South" on opposite sides of the room and
"Mason-Dixon" down the center of the
room, which indicates the Mason-Dixon
Line. The Mason-Dixon Line was first
drawn in the 1760s as the boundary
between Maryland and Pennsylvania, and
before the Civil War it was regarded as the
boundary between free and slave states.

2. Columbia has been asleep on the job. The
cartoonist is criticizing the government and
the nation for not doing enough about the
conflict between the North and the South.

3. Columbia has assigned the reading of the
United States Constitution to the students.
We know this because a number of the stu-
dents are reading it, and she has a copy of
it on her desk. Presumably she has assigned
the reading because the answer to the
North's and South's conflict is found in the
Constitution.

4. A Southern student is writing, "Let us
alone." This makes the point that the
South's main argument is about states'
rights.

5. Having the map reinforces the point that
the survival of the Union is at stake, and
that a civil war is probably on the horizon.

6. From their body positions and from how
they are scrambling back to their seats, it is
clear these students were fighting. This
may refer to the conflicts in Kansas in the
wake of the Kansas-Nebraska Act.

7. Answers will vary, but all captions should
express the idea that everyone needs to
look to the Constitution to solve the differences between the North and the South.

8. Because there are no real differences in how the two groups of students are depicted, the cartoon does not seem to favor either side.

Political Cartoon 9

1. The woman represents the Southern states. She carries a scarf labeled "The Solid South." She is stooping under the burdens of military rule and carpetbaggers.

2. The burden she is carrying is a carpetbag, in which a carpetbagger is riding. Many bayonets surround him.

3. They are "supporting" the carpetbag with their bayonets. She is chained to the rifles to symbolize Southern governments under the domination of the Northern military.

4. In the background are a ruined building, a chimney standing alone, and a sunken ship. These details are supposed to show the poverty of the South after the Civil War.

5. "Rule or Ruin" is a critical statement about the nature of the Reconstruction governments.

6. Such interpretations led Northerners to become weary of the effort and expense of maintaining a military government in the South. When the Hayes-Tilden election went to the House, Northerners agreed to remove military rule in return for Southern support for Hayes.

7. In the seven years after the end of the Civil War, Northern opinion changed from an eagerness to punish the states of the Confederacy to a desire to relieve the North of the burden of maintaining military rule in the South.

Political Cartoon 10

1. The Civil Rights Bill of 1865 is being handed to the African American.

2. The figure Columbia is handing over the Civil Rights Bill. We know this from her bracelet. She represents the spirit of America.

3. The duty of the government is to dispense equal and exact justice to everyone in all of its dealings with the people.

4. Columbia's wedding ring says "Union."

5. With the quote from *Hamlet*, Nast is saying that the United States should live up to its own ideals, and that if it plays false with African Americans—as it does when denying them equal protection of the laws, equal rights, and equal opportunities— then the country is not being true to itself.

6. The cartoonist's use of showing both hands demonstrates that nothing is being hidden or withheld. It is a symbol of utmost trust.

7. Answers will vary, but students should realize that without a shirt and jacket evident, the African American hand would have symbolized a farm laborer or other nonprofessional occupation. Nast's inclusion of the jacket and shirt sleeve emphasizes the dignity and professionalism of the hand receiving the document.

Political Cartoon 11

1. The features of the men at "The Polls" are exaggerated to show Nast's distaste for them. They are depicted as ugly, ignorant, and greedy.

2. The words "The Polls" indicate that this is a voting station.

3. The man in the middle represents the United States government. The government is made out to be a bully by being shown as a policeman ordering an innocent person to not loiter.

4. By emphasizing that the men in the background are *naturalized* while the person being ordered to move on is *native*, Nast reminds the viewer that the Native Americans were here before the Europeans and Africans, all of whom are able to vote. Nast's point is that if the naturalized can vote, surely the natives here before them should be able to.

ANSWER KEY

5. Answers will vary. Some may say "the policeman" because he is in the center and is speaking the cartoon's caption. Others will say "the Native American" because he is drawn with the greatest contrast and has a dramatic posture.

6. Answers will vary. The problems Nast is addressing are prejudice, the unjust withholding of rights, or the unlawful removal of Native Americans from their lands. The questions that students create will vary but should be general enough so that they can be asked of all three groups. The answers will vary but should indicate the root cause of the problems Nast is portraying, which is the removal of Native Americans from their lands and their being denied the basic rights other Americans have.

7. From Nast's cartoons against prejudice and for equality, we can safely predict that he would have supported the civil rights era struggles.

Political Cartoon 12

1. The cartoonist is critical of the people shown in the cartoon, viewing their actions as criminal.

2. Boss Tweed is the large man at the left. The cartoonist shows him with a bulging belly and a large gem gleaming from his vest.

3. The men in the ring are both rich and poor. The cartoon shows men of obvious wealth as well as poor people in working clothes.

4. Nast is highly critical of what he sees as corrupt government.

5. Answers will vary but may include such factors as the state of the economy, the climate of public morals and idealism, and the length in office of the incumbents.

6. Answers will vary but should include such consequences as public apathy and cynicism, inefficient and expensive government, and injustice.

Political Cartoon 13

1. The central figure in the top panel is Boss Tweed. The men around him are his top aides and cronies, presumably.

2. The man's tattered pants and worn shoes show he is poor.

3. The man is stealing bread for his family. Nast drew him stealing bread to show that he and his family do not have even the basics on which to live.

4. The man's wife and child are peeking around the corner. The child is horrified because he knows his father is going to be arrested.

5. "Wholesale" refers to the fact that Tweed and Tammany get money from the city cheap, but it also refers to them getting all the money they want, the whole thing.

6. In the top panel, the police are sanctioning major crime committed for greed. In the bottom panel, the police are enforcing the law against a needy, impoverished citizen who is trying to keep his family alive.

7. Tweed and company are exiting the New York City Treasury. Presumably they have just raided it again.

8. The question mark indicates Nast's skepticism that there will be a change in current corrupt conditions. The central issue is the corrupt condition of law and law enforcement. The law is being applied unequally and unjustly to serve the powerful and rich.

Political Cartoon 14

1. The person at left is Uncle Sam. We know this from his hat, white goatee, and striped pants. The people on the right are immigrants.

2. Wealthy Americans are greeting the immigrant by telling him not to enter.

3. The shadows represent the poor immigrants that the wealthy people were when they first arrived in the country.

Copyright © by The McGraw-Hill Companies, Inc.

INTERPRETING POLITICAL CARTOONS

77

ANSWER KEY

4. Keppler uses facial features that fit the stereotypes of what various nationalities look like. He also uses stereotypes involving the dress and occupations of the poor immigrants and the obesity of the wealthy.

5. Answers will vary but should reflect the fact that immigrants are not as welcome as they were at the time of the earlier cartoon.

6. Answers will vary but should reflect the fact that increasing immigration stirred a fearful or hypocritical reaction in those who were already established in the United States.

7. Keppler has not changed his views about immigration. He is commenting on a change in the national mood about immigration. The clearest evidence is the shadows in the bottom cartoon. Keppler uses them to criticize the hypocrisy of those keeping immigrants out.

Political Cartoon 15

1. The setting is the United States Senate.

2. The people in the front are United States senators. The people in the back represent the trusts.

3. The trusts are drawn huge and the senators small, indicating that the trusts have power over the senators.

4. The trusts are swollen and obese. Their huge bellies are labeled with the dollar sign. Their facial features are stern and forbidding.

5. The sign is an ironic comment on Lincoln's "government of the people, by the people, and for the people." The irony is in comparing the idealism of the Gettysburg Address with the sordid corruption of the trusts and their power over the Senate.

6. A sign over the doors calls it the "People's Entrance." It is barred, symbolizing that the people have been shut out and trusts have taken over.

7. The cartoonist appears to be attacking both parties. He shows senators on both sides of the aisle under the influence of the trusts.

Political Cartoon 16

1. The nurse is Mark Hanna, the wealthy Republican strategist and person many believed really controlled the presidency. He is famous for saying, "There are two things that are important in politics. The first is money, and I can't remember what the second one is."

2. The sarcasm is expressed by portraying McKinley and Roosevelt as little children who need a nurse to take care of them. Their childishness is conveyed by their size, the fact that they are playing with toys, their clothes, and their expressions.

3. The caricature is the wide, satisfied grin. With this expression, Opper conveys that as far as Hanna and the wealthy are concerned, all is going according to plan.

4. The eight years refers to two terms in the White House.

5. Opper believes they have lost all integrity because they are in the pocket of the big money interests.

6. Wealthy people often are stereotyped as greedy, and their greed is depicted by making them fat. Discuss with students if this stereotype is fair or unfair. Answers will vary. Stereotypes may be based on a real trait, but there is something inherently unfair in generalizing any trait to *all* the members of a group.

7. Answers will vary about what we can learn from the Gilded Age about money and politics. One point might be that without legislative action, nothing will really change. Another point might be that politicians are hesitant to enact campaign finance legislation because they might lose money.

78   INTERPRETING POLITICAL CARTOONS

8. The horses in the bottom cartoon are called "Militarism" and "Imperialism," two of the early twentieth century's major geopolitical issues.

Political Cartoon 17

1. The cartoon depicts the Japanese fisherman as pure evil, and exaggerates the racial features to make him frightening.

2. The cartoonist has misspelled *Monroe*.

3. The term comes from the comic strip the "Yellow Kid," which Pulitzer published and which was one of the first comics. It was used for a color-production test at Pulitzer's *New York World*. Use of color was one of the sensationalistic methods of the day.

4. The fisherman is using a gun with a bayonet as a pole and bullets as bait. He is there not to fish but to invade.

5. To say that land is "posted" is to say that an authority has restricted or forbidden access to or use of the land. The land in the cartoon is posted by the Monroe Doctrine.

6. The Monroe Doctrine warned European nations and others to stay out of the affairs of the Western Hemisphere.

7. The cartoon depicts the Japanese fisherman as sneaky when Uncle Sam lifts the hat to reveal the Japanese person underneath. Uncle Sam, on the other hand, is plastered with patriotic stars and stripes, stands tall and true, speaks the language of the common person, and takes care of business in a straightforward manner. The total effect plays purely on the emotions that respond to a simple world of villains and heroes, bad guys and good guys, which was the yellow journalistic view of the world.

Political Cartoon 18

1. The paper under Roosevelt's arm refers to the Venezuela crisis, in which Roosevelt set up negotiations to arbitrate the dispute between Venezuela and Italy, Britain, and Germany.

2. The New Diplomacy was Roosevelt's decision to pursue a more active role in foreign policy for the United States.

3. The building under Roosevelt's right arm is the United States Capitol. Its presence could show that the United States is the only important government involved, or it could suggest, by its tiny size in relation to Roosevelt, that he could proceed without interference from Congress.

4. "Speak softly and carry a big stick" is implied by the cartoon. Roosevelt carries the big stick in his hand in the form of a police nightstick.

5. Answers will vary, but many nationalities are stereotyped, including Latin Americans shown with sombreros and peasant clothes. Also stereotyped are Britain, Russia, China, Japan, Germany, and Turkey.

6. Europe, Latin America, and the United States are shown close together. The United States is in the center, and Europe and Latin America are on the fringes.

7. It supports Roosevelt, showing him as stern but beneficent.

Political Cartoon 19

1. The long goatee helps identify the male figure as Uncle Sam as does the letters "U.S." on his collar.

2. The object behind Uncle Sam is a rifle, and the U.S. insignia on his collar signifies the military. These symbols and the time period of the suffrage movement tell us that Uncle Sam is off to fight in World War I.

3. Mrs. Sam appears as a respectable, middle-class woman, not as a radical rabble-rouser. The graphic evidence is her age (between 40 and 60 years old), her hairstyle, and her dress (the modest high collar). This image supported the mainstream-suffragist argument that female voters would promote virtue and combat vice.

4. The hat is a crown, which refers to the monarchy. The message on it refers to the supposed "divine right" of men to rule over women. Divine right was a basic justification that European monarchs gave to legitimize their power and that colonial revolutionaries like Thomas Paine criticized. Both the crown and the words on it refer to the American Revolution's purpose of replacing monarchy with democracy.

5. The worry of Mrs. Sam about the humiliation of wearing an outdated hat makes the United States government (and the men-only ruling of it) appear not to be modern.

6. Answers may vary. Uncle Sam appears to hear Mrs. Sam, but he has a skeptical, slightly amused expression on his face, rather like John Adams's response to his wife's famous admonition to "Remember the ladies." By these responses, Rogers criticizes the country's response to the demands of the suffrage movement.

7. Answers will vary, but some possibilities follow. Why do you think being a woman makes me unable to do this job? What would you say to your daughter if she wanted to be a political cartoonist? Why do you think women do not need to make their own money? Why do you think only men should have full independence?

Political Cartoon 20

1. It is a fire truck. The graphic evidence is its shape, the coats that the men on it are wearing, and water pipes sticking up.

2. The figure on the wheel is Uncle Sam. His hat and goatee identify him. He is mocking the League.

3. Most of the men around Uncle Sam have joined him in taunting and mocking the League of Nations.

4. The fire refers to the territorial, ethnic, and nationalistic disputes about Poland that followed World War I. These disputes threatened peace in Europe.

5. The cartoonist is criticizing America not entering the League of Nations. The evidence is the mocking attitude of Uncle Sam and the crowd of American men, coupled with the fact that America is the cause of the League's ineffectiveness, as shown by Uncle Sam sitting on the missing wheel and the sign on the wheel. Because of this taunting, America comes off as childish.

6. The American non-participation has made the League of Nations ineffective.

Political Cartoon 21

1. Uncle Sam is the main character. He is playing the flute like the Pied Piper, encouraging immigrants to come to the United States.

2. The people on shore are Europe's nobility and wealthy classes. They are happy because they are getting rid of people they do not want.

3. The immigrants are stereotyped in the worst way as rats, a characterization that the Nazis would use about Jews. They are also caricatured as criminals, arsonists, and terrorists by what they have in their mouths.

4. Answers will vary. The factors mentioned include the following: competition for jobs, immigrants working for lower wages, wages being driven down, and fear of different political and social philosophies. Factors not mentioned will vary but may include opposition to immigration from countries that have sponsored or harbored terrorists.

5. A cartoon comparing immigrants to rats and depicting them as criminals of various kinds would be considered very offensive today.

6. There was probably not much, if any, outcry when the cartoon first appeared. Americans today are generally more sensitive to ethnic and racial labeling and less accepting of intolerance.

Political Cartoon 22

1. They are recent immigrants to the United States.

2. Native Americans, whose presence in the Americas dates back thousands of years, are the only non-immigrants. The man in the middle is the descendant of immigrants.

3. People on left: confused yet dignified, shown by unemotional pose in response to middle person's anger. Person in middle: angry, shown by angry gesture, large bold type, exclamation mark. Person on right: dry wit, arms crossed, smaller-type words.

4. The cartoonist points to the difference between the anger of the man in the middle against immigrants and the obvious fact that he is a descendant of immigrants.

5. Answers will vary but should refer to the increase of immigration in recent years and the increase in undocumented immigration.

6. Answers will vary but should contain the elements of irony.

Political Cartoon 23

1. The man on the park bench represents the victims of the bank failures during the Great Depression, which left millions destitute.

2. Many people who were unemployed and homeless slept on park benches. The reference hints that this person will end up in that condition.

3. The facts that he is well-dressed and well-groomed and is smoking a pipe make him out to be a solid, thoughtful citizen.

4. The squirrel symbolizes prudence. The squirrel is a good symbol for this virtue because squirrels store up food during good times for the winter, a time of scarcity.

5. Answers may include overproduction of agricultural and manufactured goods; consumers buying goods on installment and going into debt; both consumers and banks buying stocks on margin; the actions of the Federal Reserve, which lowered interest rates and encouraged bad loans; and so on.

6. For part of his first hundred days, Roosevelt closed banks, declaring a "bank holiday." The most important long-term measure to prevent citizens from becoming victims of bank failure was establishing the Federal Deposit Insurance Corporation.

Political Cartoon 24

1. The horse refers to the trick the Greeks played on the Trojans to end the Trojan War. A large wooden horse appeared at the gates of Troy, and it appeared that the Greeks had given up and gone home. Of course, Greek warriors were inside the horse, and after it was brought into the city, the Greeks snuck out under the cover of night and sacked the city.

2. The gate to the city is the Constitution, and American citizens guard the walls.

3. The most important pieces of New Deal legislation that were declared partially unconstitutional were the Agricultural Adjustment Act and the National Industrial Recovery Act.

4. The person in the rear of the bottom cartoon is wearing a mortarboard, which identifies him as a university professor.

5. Answers will vary. The person holding the mask is wearing a fedora and has a darker smirk that might be associating him with organized crime. The other person has a cigar and a hat that identifies him as a smoke-filled-room dealmaker. More specifically, Huey Long wore this kind of hat.

6. In the bottom cartoon, the expression on the mask is warm and benign. However, the expressions of the men behind the mask are greedy.

7. Both of these cartoons express the idea that the New Dealers are sneaky and devious.

The cartoonists are telling us that the New Deal has hidden agendas and to beware of them.

8. The cartoonist is highly critical of the New Deal.

Political Cartoon 25

1. The three men on the left are Mussolini, Hitler, and Tojo. The three men in the upper right-hand corner are Stalin, Roosevelt, and Churchill.

2. Most people are afraid of going into surgery. The Axis leaders are afraid. The signs are their facial expressions and the fact that they are sweating.

3. The helmet on the patient's stomach and the combination of the fact that he is bandaged from head to toe with the words "African Front" indicate that the patient being wheeled out is German.

4. Stalin is identified by his moustache; Mussolini by his large, bald head; and Tojo by his teeth.

5. Both Hitler and Tojo are pointing at Mussolini to indicate that Italy should be next. It was. By the time France was invaded, the Allies had worked their way up from Sicily to Rome and had captured Italy.

6. Stalin looks eager to "operate," while Churchill looks determined.

7. A war zone is also called a "theater of operations," and military actions are called "operations." The cartoon's pun, then, turns on the difference between a medical and military operation. The first is meant to heal; the second is meant to defeat the enemy. Hence the people coming out of this cartoon's operating room are in worse shape than the ones going in.

8. Hitler's size indicates that Germany is the most powerful foe and the leader of the Axis forces.

Political Cartoon 26

1. The person in the cartoon is Senator Joseph McCarthy from Wisconsin.

2. The term "doctored photo" refers to a picture that has been changed to represent something different from the original. In this case, McCarthy has superimposed images on photographs to make government officials appear to be friendly with Communists.

3. McCarthy is caricatured with a dark scowl and a heavy, almost unshaven beard.

4. The title is from McCarthy's famous gesture of holding up a piece of paper he claimed was a list of names of Communists working in the United States government. He never handed the list over, so these words have come to symbolize his dishonesty and trickery.

5. The main point of the cartoon is that McCarthy has in his hands not a list of Communists in government but rather illegal and unethical methods to draw publicity to himself. He will be brought down by his own deeds and methods, because they show he is a thug and a fraud.

6. The cartoonist uses the stereotypes of being unshaven and having dirty or singed hands to show that Senator McCarthy is dishonest. Being unclean is a common association with being a criminal. Someone who is corrupt is "unclean" or "dirty," and after doing something illegal, a person has "dirty hands."

7. Like Vietnam did for foreign military engagements, the McCarthy Red Scare has put America more on guard against his type of demagoguery and made Americans more tolerant of political differences.

Political Cartoon 27

1. Mauldin has drawn the statue of Abraham Lincoln.

2. The statue is located in the Lincoln Memorial in Washington, D.C. The location helps convey the idea that the entire country is in mourning.

3. Lincoln's hands over his face and his crumpled pose indicate that Lincoln is weeping. On an obvious level, Mauldin is conveying the deep grief of the country over President Kennedy's assassination. On a deeper level, the hands over the face convey shame and a desire to not acknowledge the event, as if it is too much to absorb.

4. Answers may vary. The shadow appears to be of a hooded figure, symbolizing death.

5. Answers may vary. Having a statue come to life indicates how profound and powerful the event of the assassination was for the nation's heart and soul. Even dead stone weeps.

6. By associating Kennedy with Lincoln, Mauldin makes clear that America has just lost a great civil rights president. The association works especially well because of Lincoln's assassination. This fact creates a personal connection between Kennedy and Lincoln that strengthens the political message of the cartoon.

7. Answers may vary. The silence of the cartoon indicates that the Kennedy assassination is so horrible as to be unspeakable. The absence of text also allows for the viewer to bring in his or her emotions freely for interpreting and responding to the cartoon. The silence allows the viewer to share in the grief, not just to look at or think about the cartoon.

Political Cartoon 28

1. The South Vietnamese and the United States are the "forces of freedom," whereas the North Vietnamese and the Viet Cong are the "people's democracies." The names are so close in meaning that they could be switched. This fact emphasizes how the claims of each side about the purpose of the war are empty.

2. The family's house has been destroyed, and they are trapped inside.

3. The characters, especially the adults, are drawn with Asian features, and the man is wearing a hat commonly worn in Vietnam.

4. Answers may vary. Children increase the emotional response to the cartoon in two ways: (a) because children signify hope and promise, they naturally heighten our empathy in general; and (b) children's innocence and vulnerability intensify our horror at war.

5. The cartoons do make the same point, which is that wars do not always help the people for whom the governments say the war is being fought.

6. There are two similarities between the cartoons: the forces that are fighting are anonymous and identical, and the characters look perplexed and dumbfounded by the fighting.

7. The cartoons are drawn from the point of view of the people for whom the war *supposedly* is being fought.

Political Cartoon 29

1. The two people are the town sheriff and a voting official.

2. A literacy test determines whether one can read.

3. The irony is that the person who is supposed to be monitoring the voting process and administering literacy tests cannot read.

4. The cartoonist has drawn the sheriff with a large belly, cigar, and casual stance to play on the stereotype of the "good ol' boy." The seated voting official has been drawn as unkempt and with dark eyes—a typical

caricature of someone who is uneducated or who has something to hide.

5. Literacy tests required would-be voters to be able to read before being allowed to vote. Many African Americans in the South had substandard "separate-but-not-equal" schools and education. Thus, many African Americans had poor reading skills. In addition, the voting officials giving the literacy test often selected very difficult passages for would-be voters to attempt to read. In this way, voting officials could prevent African Americans from voting.

6. The basic issue is that progress in civil rights has often been slow and misguided.

Political Cartoon 30

1. The men are supposedly the committee assigned the task of writing the Declaration of Independence. The cartoon has "adapted" the scene from J.L.G. Ferris's famous painting *Drafting the Declaration of Independence*. Most students will recognize Benjamin Franklin, who is speaking, and Thomas Jefferson, the "Tom" to whom Franklin is referring.

2. They are reading from the Declaration of Independence.

3. She symbolizes the status of women in the United States.

4. Answers will vary, but students may touch upon the lack of equality of women in the United States and the use of only the word "men" in the document.

5. The irony is that the words "All men are created equal" are beautiful only if one was a white male at the time of the writing of the Declaration of Independence.

6. Answers will vary, but students should provide reasons for their responses.

Political Cartoon 31

1. The reference to blazing a trail conjures up cowhands, the American migration west,

and the importance of the frontier. The reference to destiny recalls the American doctrine of Manifest Destiny.

2. With this question, Cobb shows how automobiles are marketed by association with a macho kind of masculinity.

3. The name has two meanings. As a product name, it conveys how powerfully the car zooms down the road. As a commentary by the cartoonist, it helps convey the laughable difference between name and reality, and how fossil fuel consumption is burning up the environment.

4. The driver has been grocery shopping, which we know from the bags in her passenger seat. Her destination shows an ironic contrast between what the billboard promises and actually owning the car.

5. "Mach 8" refers to a very high rate of speed. Mach numbers are used to measure the speed of high-speed vehicles. A Mach number refers to the speed of sound; Mach 1, therefore, is the speed of sound—1,087 feet per second (at sea level). Mach 8 is eight times as fast as the speed of sound. The term *Mach* gained popularity after Chuck Yeager broke the sound barrier in a jet in 1947. Given that the cartoon was published in the 1970s, "Mach 8" might also refer to being "macho."

6. Blazer, Sonoma, Cherokee, Ranger, and Durango are some of the recent automobile names with frontier references. Many such names are given to SUVs.

7. The cartoon exposes the tremendous gap between what products promise and what they deliver. The cartoonist is telling us there is a destructive lie at the heart of consumer society.

8. The anti-consumerism, environmentalism, and ironic use of iconic parts of American identity support the view that the cartoonist is a liberal.

9. Students' advertisements will vary.

Political Cartoon 32

1. General Westmoreland was the commander of U.S. forces in Vietnam for a number of years and is the American general most identified with the Vietnam War. His saluting tells us he is in the military; his medals tell us he is a high-ranking officer; the stars on his hat tell us he is a general.

2. The Sandinistas were the left-wing, Marxist forces that had assumed power in Nicaragua in 1979. President Reagan tried to combat them by funding the contras, a guerrilla force within Nicaragua.

3. The man on the horse is President Reagan. His expression is thoroughly optimistic, which the cartoonist wants us to understand as meaning that Reagan is being naïve and gullible.

4. When Westmoreland says that the Sandinista troops counts are acceptable and we are winning the hearts and minds of the people, he is repeating what he said during the war in Vietnam. The reference to the "light at the end of the tunnel" refers to a common expression meaning that the end is in sight, and it was a statement Henry Kissinger used about Vietnam a full three years before the last American troops left Saigon. The expression has been used unreliably so often that it is almost always taken ironically. Since Vietnam, these statements make us think of getting into a protracted, ultimately unsuccessful military involvement.

5. This device allows Oliphant to reinforce the theme of the cartoon by commenting on it.

6. The figure to Westmoreland's left represents the right-wing dictator that the contras would support. The heavy beard, sunglasses, cigar, and grenades across his chest all indicate stereotypically that he is a corrupt Latin American dictator who keeps political power by military and police sup-

port. Oliphant's point of view is negative toward this figure.

7. Reagan's word "Bully" refers to Teddy Roosevelt and, therefore, San Juan Hill. The president's clothes and bugle also refer to Roosevelt and San Juan Hill because they are of his era's cavalry. Oliphant makes this reference because both Cuba and Nicaragua are in Latin America.

8. Answers will very but should relate to America not learning from its history of trying to determine the nature of foreign governments.

Political Cartoon 33

1. This cartoon is addressing the environment.

2. The cartoonist implies that it is trendy to protect the environment now, but that sentiment may not be long-lasting.

3. The irony is that Americans—who labeled Native Americans as savages—are themselves the savages who have treated the land with disrespect.

4. Answers will vary, but students will probably understand that adding more illustrations would have detracted readers from the simple yet powerful message of the cartoon.

5. Answers will vary, but students should mention that Americans have assumed that their environment would not change dramatically, in spite of their habits and heavy consumption.

6. The Native American is stereotyped by the long hair, feathers, and facial structure. Students will probably agree that the stereotype works well in this instance, because it reinforces the "savage" image of Native Americans that most people have held throughout American history, while at the same time debunking the stereotype by making the Native American appear noble and dignified under these circumstances.

ANSWER KEY

Political Cartoon 34

1. The candidates are Bill Clinton, George H.W. Bush, and Ross Perot.

2. The candidates, drawn in extreme caricatures, are all grinning with their eyes closed.

3. They will try to condense their ideas into short memorable phrases and use wit to impress their audience.

4. Bill Clinton was Democrat, George H.W. Bush was Republican, and Ross Perot was the Reform Party candidate.

5. Even the debate mediator expects nothing more than sound-bites, slogans, put-downs, and zingers. The cartoonist is pointing out that the American people have similar expectations of presidential debates.

6. To hold people's attention, television moves quickly from scene to scene and idea to idea. Television producers do not allow time for lengthy responses to political questions.

Political Cartoon 35

1. The person is Fidel Castro.

2. He is waiting for other Communist leaders to arrive at a reunion.

3. Answers will vary, but most students will comment on Castro's seeming ignorance as to what has happened in Eastern Europe and the former Soviet Union.

4. The cartoon is saying that communism as a form of government is dwindling among the countries of the world.

5. The countries whose leaders would have been present in 1985 include East Germany and all of the satellite republics of the former Soviet Union.

6. Answers will vary, but students should provide reasons for their suggestions.

7. Answers will vary but may be similar to: Last Dance for Communists, A Reunion of One, and so on.

Political Cartoon 36

1. The biggest symbol of apathy is the empty auditorium.

2. The empty auditorium is an effective symbol of apathy because it shows that even an event meant to draw voters does not appeal to the apathetic public.

3. The cartoonist evidently feels that voter apathy is widespread and that such events as public forums and debates no longer attract interest from the public.

4. Answers will vary but may include the idea that the democratic process is less effective with less voter participation, and the danger that small, vocal groups could then wield undue influence.

5. Answers will vary but might include the dissatisfaction of voters with government and elected officials.

6. Answers will vary but could include: No Vote for Apathy, Too Busy for Democracy?, Where Have All the Voters Gone?

INTERPRETING POLITICAL CARTOONS